Ally McBeal
FOR ONCE IN MY I
featuring VONDA SHEPARD

16 songs arranged for Piano, Vocal and Guitar

Edited by Anna Joyce
Folio Design by Dominic Brookman

Published 2001

© International Music Publications Ltd
Griffin House 161 Hammersmith Road London W6 8BS England

£12.99

For Once In My Life

Words by Ronald Miller
Music by Orlando Murden

strong._____ For once I can touch what my heart_____ used to dream of_____

-more._____ For once I can say_____ this is

For once I can say_____ this is

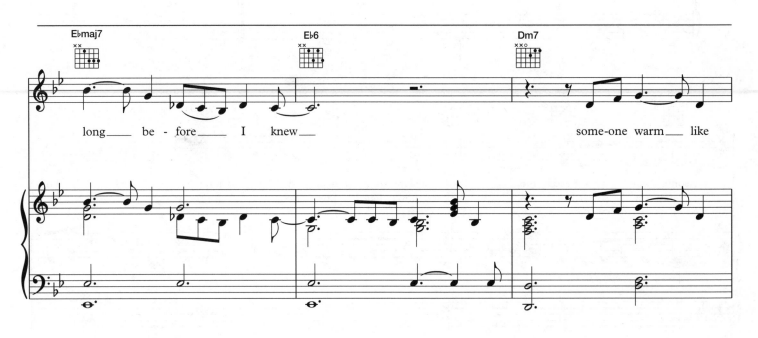

long_____ be - fore_____ I knew_____ some-one warm_____ like

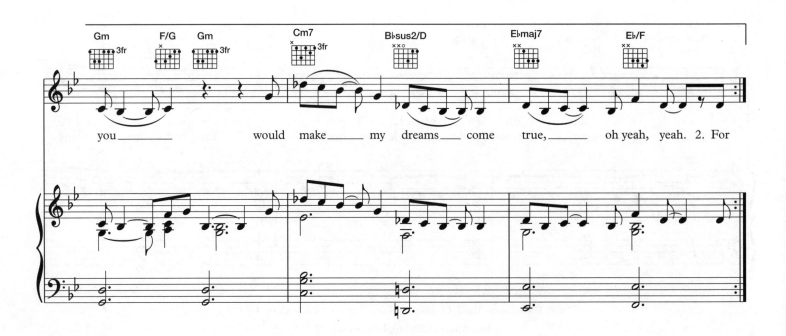

you_____ would make_____ my dreams_____ come true,_____ oh yeah, yeah. 2. For

Home Again

Words and Music by
Carole King

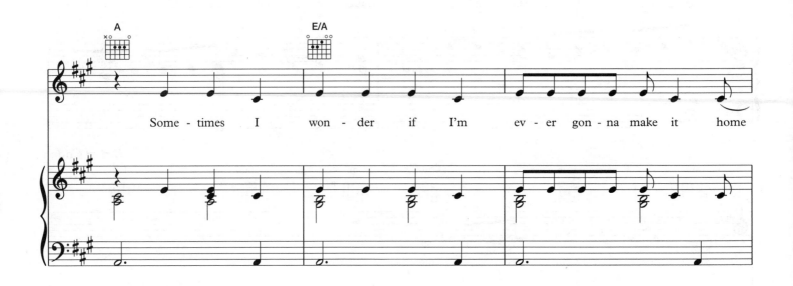

Some - times I won - der if I'm ev - er gon - na make it home

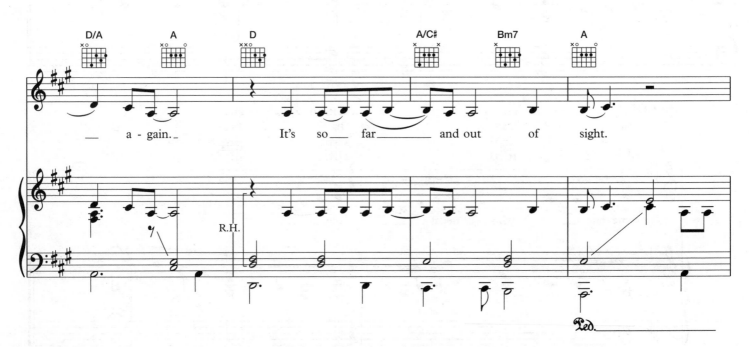

___ a - gain. ___ It's so ___ far ___ and out of sight.

Snow is cold, rain _____ is _____

Chances Are

Words and Music by
Bob Seger

1. Chan - ces are___ you'll find___ me some - where on your road to - night, seems I al - ways end___ up driv - ing by.___ Ev - er since___ I've known you, it just seems you're on___ the way,___

Don't Think Twice, It's All Right

Words and Music by
Bob Dylan

Every Breath You Take

Words and Music by
Gordon Sumner

Snakes

Words and Music by
Robert Downey Jr

You have bo - dy, you give soul,_____

30

You And Me

Words and Music by
Vonda Shepard

1. Part of me ___ wants to break the ice   and part of me wants to leave it ex-act-ly how it stands.
2. Part of me ___ wants to break these chains   and part of me wants to keep 'em locked up tight.

Part of me ___ wants to roll the dice ___   and part of me wants to leave 'em curled up in my hands. Well
Part of me ___ wants to stop these rains ___   and part of me wants them to fall ___ all ___ night.

Reason To Believe

Words and Music by
Tim Hardin

How Can You Mend A Broken Heart

Words and Music by
Barry Gibb and Robin Gibb

1. I can think of young-er days
2. I can still__ feel the breeze

when live__ for my life
that rus-tles through the trees

When The Heartache Is Over

Words and Music by
John Reid and Graham Stack

Rive Droite Music Ltd, Surrey KT1 4AE and Universal Music Publishing Ltd, London W6 8JA

heart-ache is ov - er, I know__ I won't be miss-ing you.__

Won't look ov - er my shoul - der, 'cause I know____ that I can

live with - out____ you,____ yeah.__ (*Vocal ad lib.*)

repeat to fade

You're The First, The Last, My Everything

Words and Music by
Barry White, Tony Sepe and Sterling Radcliffe

Love Is Alive

Words and Music by
Gary Wright

Love is a-live,__ love is a-live, yeah,

love is a-live,__ love is a-live, yeah.   *(Vocal ad lib.)*

Alone Again (Naturally)

Words and Music by
Gilbert O'Sullivan

Can We Still Be Friends

Words and Music by
Todd Rundgren

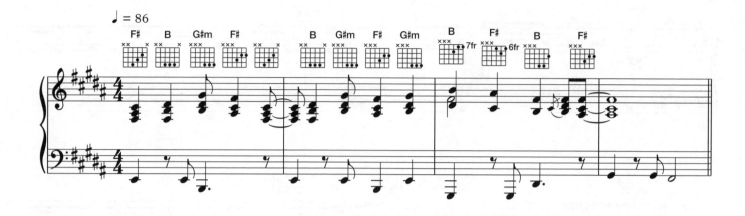

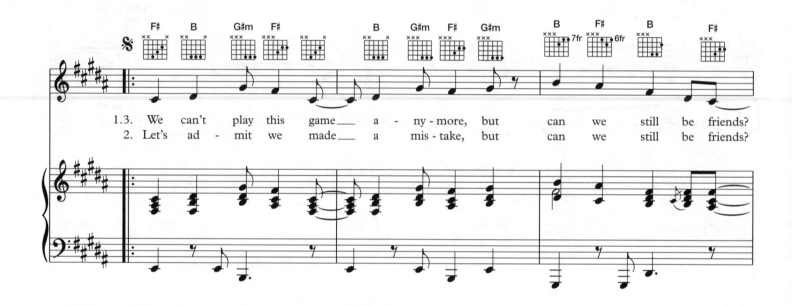

1.3. We can't play this game a-ny-more, but can we still be friends?
2. Let's ad-mit we made a mis-take, but can we still be friends?

Things just can't go on like be-fore, but can we still be friends?
Heart-break's ne-ver ea-sy to take, but can we still be friends?

Can we still be friends?

It's Not Unusual

Words and Music by
Gordon Mills and Les Reed

Boom Boom

Words and Music by
Antonio Montoya, Estéfano, Poncho Abaldonato,
Raphael Abaldonato, Antoine Santiago and Fevrier Fernadez

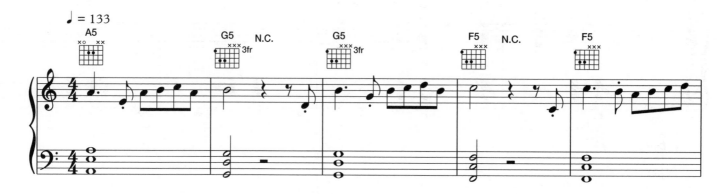

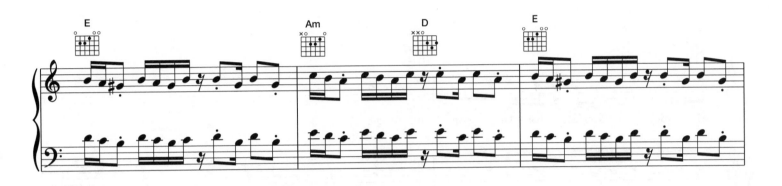

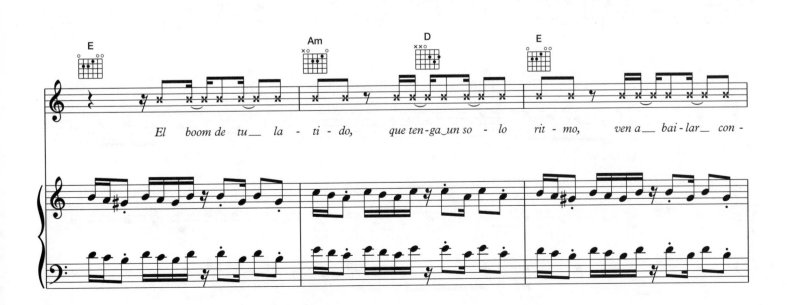

El boom de tu__ la - ti - do,   que ten-ga_un so - lo   rit - mo,   ven a__ bai - lar__ con -

Also Available

Heart and Soul:
New Songs from Ally McBeal
featuring Vonda Shepard
Piano/Vocal/Guitar
(7269A)   ISBN: 1859098649

More great songs from the Emmy Award-winning comedy! Titles are: Read Your Mind - 100 Tears Away - Someday We'll Be Together - To Sir, with Love (duet with Al Green) - Sweet Inspiration - Crying - Vincent (Starry Starry Night) - What Becomes of the Brokenhearted - Confetti - Baby Don't You Break My Heart Slow (duet with Emily Saliers of the Indigo Girls) - This Is Crazy Now - This Old Heart of Mine (Is Weak for You) - I Know Him by Heart - Searchin' My Soul.

Television Selections
featuring Vonda Shepard
Piano/Vocal/Guitar
(6704A)   ISBN: 1859096816

A collection of songs from the successful soundtrack album of the Emmy award-winning comedy series featuring the vocals of Vonda Shepard. Titles are: Searchin' My Soul - Ask the Lonely - Walk Away Renee - Hooked on a Feeling - You Belong to Me - The Wildest Times of the World - Someone You Use - The End of the World - Tell Him - Neighborhood - Will You Marry Me? - It's in His Kiss (The Shoop Shoop Song) - I Only Want to Be with You - Maryland.

Available now from all good music shops

AMB1

Saw these fantastic books today!
Must buy them immediately!

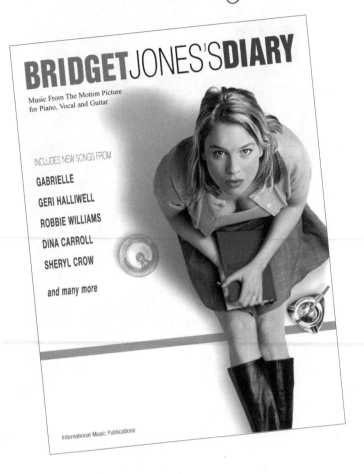

19 SONGS FROM THE MOTION PICTURE
ARRANGED FOR PIANO, VOCAL AND GUITAR
9296A   ISBN 1-84328-017-5

GABRIELLE Out Of Reach
ARETHA FRANKLIN Respect
GERI HALLIWELL It's Raining Men
ROBBIE WILLIAMS Have You Met Miss Jones?
CHAKA KHAN I'm Every Woman
PRETENDERS Don't Get Me Wrong
SHERYL CROW Kiss That Girl
SHELBY LYNNE Killin' Kind
DINA CARROLL Someone Like You
ROBBIE WILLIAMS Not Of This Earth
ANDY WILLIAMS Can't Take My Eyes Off You
ROSEY Love
DIANA ROSS & MARVIN GAYE
Stop, Look, Listen (To Your Heart)
SHELBY LYNNE Dreamsome
PATRICK DOYLE It's Only A Diary
ALISHA'S ATTIC Pretender Got My Heart
JAMIE O'NEAL All By Myself
ARTFUL DODGER & ROBBIE CRAIG FEAT. CRAIG DAVID
Woman Trouble
AARON SOUL Ring, Ring, Ring

THE MOTION PICTURE SING-ALONG BOOK
5 SONGS WITH SING-ALONG CD
9537A   ISBN 1-84328-114-7

JAMIE O'NEAL All By Myself
PRETENDERS Don't Get Me Wrong
GERI HALLIWELL It's Raining Men
GABRIELLE Out Of Reach
ROBBIE WILLIAMS Have You Met Miss Jones?

AVAILABLE NOW FROM ALL GOOD MUSIC SHOPS

BJ1